the Garfield Gallery

Jim Davis

6

HODDER AND STOUGHTON
LONDON   SYDNEY   AUCKLAND   TORONTO

British Library Cataloguing in Publication Data

Davis, Jim, *1945–*
    The Garfield gallery 6.
    1. American wit and humour. Pictorial
    I. Title
    741.5'973

    ISBN 0-340-50124-3

First published in Great Britain 1989

Published by Hodder and Stoughton Children's Books,
a division of Hodder and Stoughton Ltd,
Mill Road, Dunton Green, Sevenoaks, Kent TN13 2YA

Printed in Italy by New Interlitho S.p.A., Milan

SLAM!

© 1980 United Feature Syndicate, Inc.   JIM DAVIS

9-27   JIM DAVIS

GOBBLE!
GOBBLE!
GOBBLE!

© 1980 United Feature Syndicate, Inc.

THANKS FOR LEAVING A WING, GARFIELD

WHAT ARE FRIENDS FOR?

HOW ABOUT DINNER TONIGHT, DOC?

SURE

IF THERE'S NOTHING GOOD ON TELEVISION

© 1980 United Feature Syndicate, Inc.

DID YOU HEAR THAT, GARFIELD? SHE PRACTICALLY THREW HERSELF AT ME!

PRAY FOR RERUNS, HOTSHOT

9-29   JIM DAVIS

JUST ONCE I'D LIKE TO GO ON A DATE WITHOUT GARFIELD

JIM DAVIS

© 1980 United Feature Syndicate, Inc.

WHERE TO, SIR?

9-30

PAYS TO BE ORGANIZED

WELCOME TO NATIONAL FAT WEEK.

9-8

THIS IS THE WEEK ALL OF YOU, MY FAT BROTHERS AND SISTERS, CELEBRATE YOUR BIG, ROUND, BEAUTIFUL BODIES

REMEMBER, YOU'RE NOT OVERWEIGHT, EVERYONE ELSE IS UNDERNOURISHED

© 1980 United Feature Syndicate, Inc. JIM DAVIS

THIS IS NATIONAL FAT WEEK. ARISE, FAT PEOPLE!

9-9

LET US AVERT OUR NATION'S INSENSITIVITY TOWARD FAT PEOPLE!

LET US MAKE FUN OF BALD PEOPLE!

© 1980 United Feature Syndicate, Inc. JIM DAVIS

HERE'S A NATIONAL FAT WEEK HANDY FACT...

9-10

60% OF THE PEOPLE IN OUR NATION ARE INVOLVED IN SOME WAY WITH THE FOOD INDUSTRY

THAT'S RIGHT. EATING IS NOT ONLY FUN, IT'S PATRIOTIC!

© 1980 United Feature Syndicate, Inc. JIM DAVIS

THIS YEAR, LET'S CELEBRATE NATIONAL FAT WEEK BY STAMPING OUT FAT JOKES

9-11

LET'S FACE IT, FATTIES...

WE SHOULD BE ABLE TO STAMP OUT ANYTHING WE WISH

© 1980 United Feature Syndicate, Inc. JIM DAVIS

GARFIELD'S HISTORY OF DOGS

DURING THE STONE AGE, DOGS WERE USED FOR HUNTING MUCH AS THEY ARE TODAY

BARK BARK

9-3

GRRRR

© 1980 United Feature Syndicate, Inc.

TIMES WERE TOUGH THEN

STOMP!

JIM DAVIS

GARFIELD'S HISTORY OF DOGS

CONTRARY TO POPULAR BELIEF...

9-4

THE FIRST DOGS WERE **HAPPY** TO MEET THE FIRST CAT

FOR, UNTIL THEN, ALL THEY HAD TO CHASE UP TREES WERE ROCKS

ARF

© 1980 United Feature Syndicate, Inc.   JIM DAVIS

GARFIELD'S HISTORY OF DOGS

JIM DAVIS   © 1980 United Feature Syndicate, Inc.

THE FIRST FIRE HYDRANT

9-5

DOGS' HISTORIC ROLES AS HUNTERS, PROTECTORS, TRACKERS, LABORERS AND COMPANIONS HAVE CULMINATED TO MAKE MODERN DOG WHAT HE IS TODAY

JIM DAVIS   © 1980 United Feature Syndicate, Inc.

IT COULD JUST MAKE YOU CRY

9-6

SIT UP AND BEG FOR THE KITTY MUNCHY, GARFIELD

3-23

TELL YOU WHAT. YOU GIVE ME THE MUNCHY AND I'LL LET YOU KEEP YOUR FACE

I KNEW WE COULD ARRIVE AT A MUTUALLY ACCEPTABLE COMPROMISE

JIM DAVIS   1979 United Feature Syndicate, Inc.

DANCE FOR ME, GARFIELD

NOT A CHANCE

JIM DAVIS   © 1979 United Feature Syndicate, Inc.

IF YOU WON'T, I'M SURE ODIE WOULD BE HAPPY TO

YOU HAVE TO KNOW WHAT MOTIVATES A CAT

THIS IS DEMEANING

TAPPITY TAPPITY

3-24

AH, IT'S EARLY MORNING FOR THE CAPED AVENGER

RING!

© 1979 United Feature Syndicate, Inc.

THE CAPED AVENGER WHO SEARCHES OUT EVIL WHEREVER IT MAY LURK

THE LATE-MORNING EVIL, THAT IS

3-26   JIM DAVIS

THE CAPED AVENGER SEES FOOD!

© 1979 United Feature Syndicate, Inc.   3-27

IN ORDER TO FIGHT EVIL, THE CAPED AVENGER NEEDS FOOD FOR STRENGTH

LOTS AND **LOTS** OF STRENGTH!

JIM DAVIS

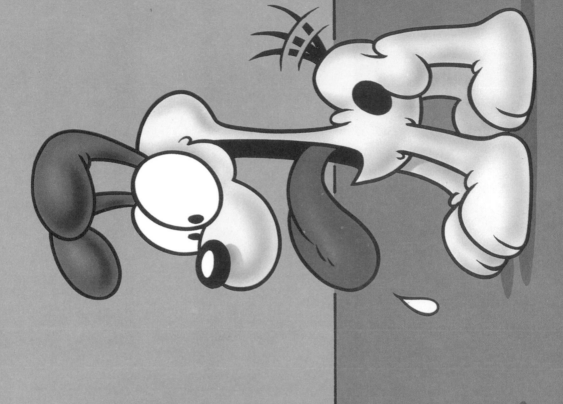

No

Smoking

MONDAY

REEKS

JIM DAVIS

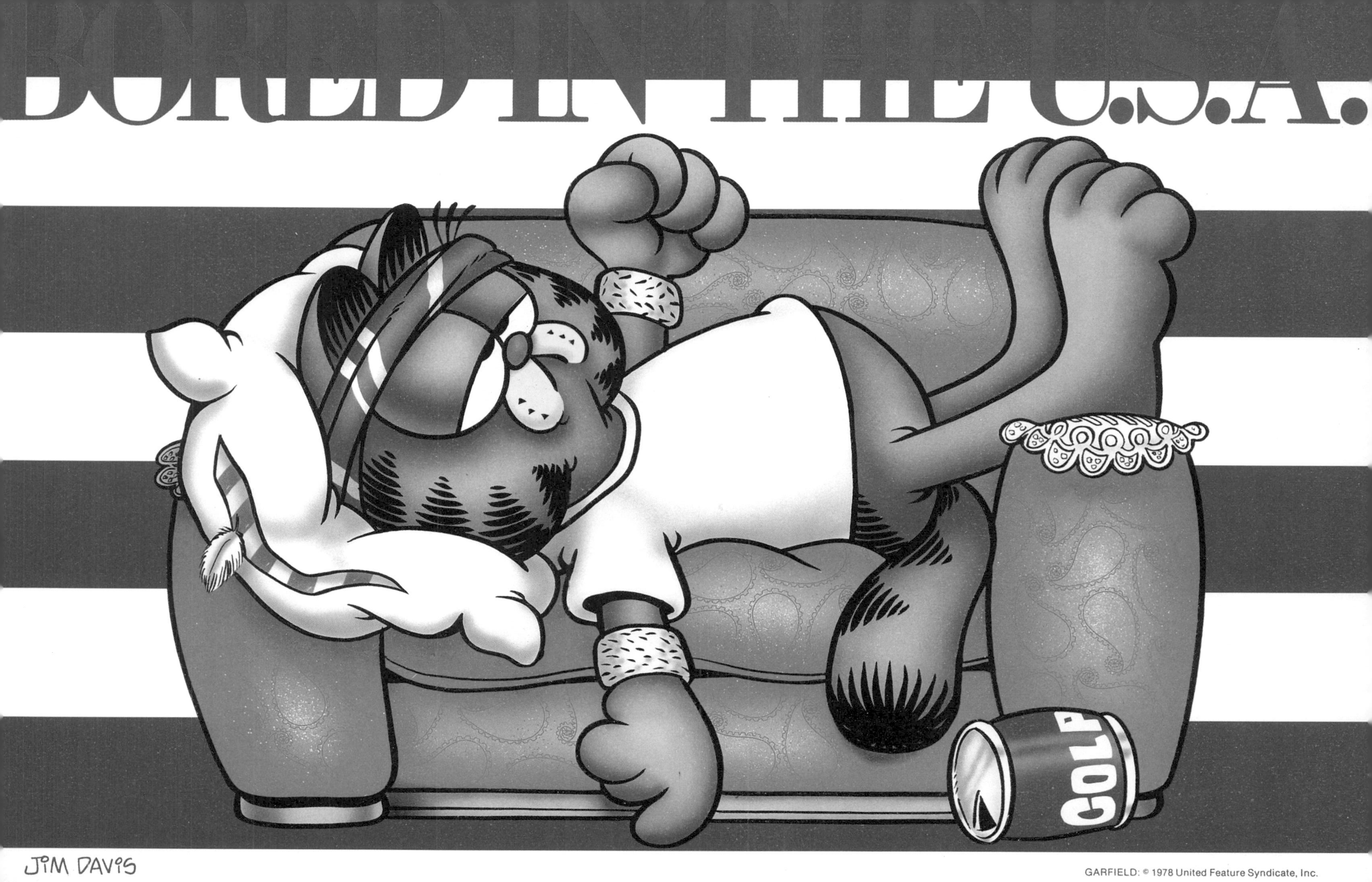
BORED IN THE U.S.A.
GOLF
JIM DAVIS

PURRRR

RRRON

TAPPITY
TAPPITY
TAPPITY

TAPPITY
TAPPITY
TAPPITY

5-6

SCRATCH!
SCRATCH!
SCRATCH!
SCRATCH!

GOOD MORNING, SUNSHINE.
WELCOME TO ANOTHER
GLORIOUS, FUN-FILLED DAY
WITH YOUR FAVORITE PET!

I'M SO HAPPY
TO OWN A CAT,
I COULD JUST
THROW UP

JIM DAVIS

THE DIRECT APPROACH IS THE BEST APPROACH

JIM DAVIS

HOP HOP

THAT'S THE THING ABOUT CANNED SALMON
HOP

IT'S EASIER TO CATCH WHEN IT HEADS UPSTREAM TO SPAWN
8-1
JIM DAVIS

GRRRR
© 1980 United Feature Syndicate, Inc.
8-2

ROWR!

ONE OF THESE DAYS THIS FIERCE ROUTINE'S GONNA GET ME CREAMED
YIP YIP YIP
JIM DAVIS

YOU'LL HAVE TO ADMIT, GARFIELD...
8-8

NOW THAT YOU'RE ON A DIET, YOU'RE FEELING BETTER ABOUT YOURSELF
YOU BET

ASIDE FROM THE HUNGER, DIZZINESS AND WEAKNESS, I'M HAVING A BALL
JIM DAVIS
© 1980 United Feature Syndicate, Inc.

YOU'RE THE CORRECT WEIGHT...
8-9
© 1980 United Feature Syndicate, Inc.

FOR AN AIRCRAFT CARRIER, HA-HA

I SHOULDN'T HAVE SAID THAT
JIM DAVIS

GROWL

THE CAT CRAVES FRESH MEAT

4-29

WHAT-HO, THE CAT SENSES UNSUSPECTING QUARRY O'ER YON KNOLL

© 1979 United Feature Syndicate, Inc.

JIM DAVIS

COILING LIKE A SPRING, HE PREPARES TO LUNGE

STEELY SINEWS PROPEL HIM TOWARD HIS HELPLESS PREY

ONCE AGAIN A CAT'S PRIMAL INSTINCTS PROVIDE SUSTENANCE